CROSSROAD PUZZLERS

CROSSROAD PUZZLERS

DAVID WEBSTER

PUBLISHED FOR

THE AMERICAN MUSEUM OF NATURAL HISTORY

 THE NATURAL HISTORY PRESS

GARDEN CITY, NEW YORK, 1967

The Natural History Press, publisher for The American Museum of Natural History, is a division of Doubleday & Company, Inc. Directed by a joint editorial board made up of members of the staff of both the Museum and Doubleday, the Natural History Press publishes books and periodicals in all branches of the life and earth sciences, including anthropology and astronomy. The Natural History Press has its editorial offices at The American Museum of Natural History, Central Park West at 79th Street, New York, N.Y. 10024, and its business offices at 501 Franklin Avenue, Garden City, N.Y.

INTRODUCTION

There is a lot to see when you go on a car trip. The photographs in the first part of *Crossroad Puzzlers* should give you ideas about some things to look for. Most of the pictures were taken in New York, Massachusetts, and Maine. Readers who live in Southern states should remember that a few of the questions about roads and signs are connected with snow removal.

The second part of this book contains suggestions for playing games in the car and for doing science experiments while traveling. Notice that you will need certain materials in order to do many of the activities.

Take along *Crossroad Puzzlers* when you go on your next trip. What interesting things can you and your family find along the highway?

PHOTO CREDITS

PICTURE SECTION:

Things to Look for Along the Highway

CARS AND TRUCKS

What does this truck do?

What do these trucks carry?

Look for other unusual trucks.

Why do these trucks have steering wheels on the "wrong" side?

Can you find any other right-hand steering wheels?

When are the little wheels on the trailer used?

Why are the rear wheels of this truck raised when it is not loaded?

Why are there big treads on tractor tires, and . . .

no treads at all on the tires of drag racers?

Why is the name printed backwards?

What are the numbers on the roof for?

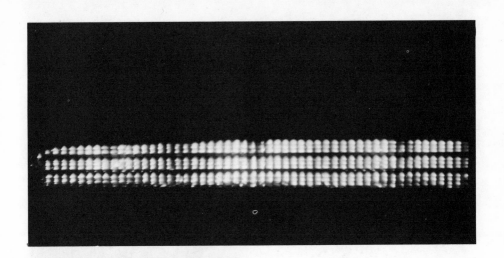

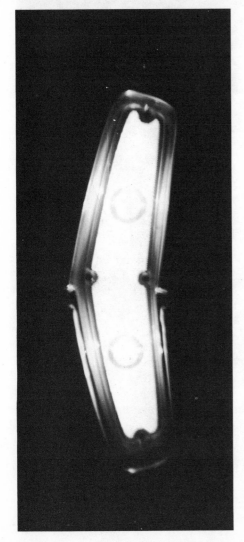

To what makes of cars do these tail-lights belong?

At night, see if you can identify cars by the shape of their taillights.

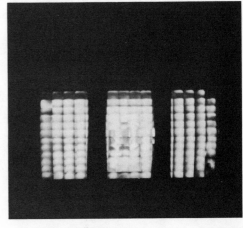

What happened to this truck?

Which car probably ran into the back of a truck? What did the other one hit?

Have you ever seen a car with a door that looks different from the rest of the car? Why is this?

Why do cars often rust only in certain places?

Look for other spots where cars get rusty.

"Sorry, parking lot filled."

What happened to these cars?

ANSWERS

Page 9

The truck is used to collect the money from parking meters. The long tube works like a vacuum cleaner to suck up the coins when the meter is opened.

Page 10

TOP: The truck is used for carrying large sheets of plate glass.

BOTTOM: Trucks like this one are built to move piles of lumber.

Page 11

TOP: The mail truck makes frequent stops to collect mail from sidewalk mailboxes. The right-hand steering wheel makes it easier for the driver to get in and out of his truck.

BOTTOM: A right-hand steering wheel on the street sweeper enables the driver to see the street close to the curb when he is cleaning it. Why do almost all trucks in Great Britain have steering wheels on the right side?

Page 12

TOP: When the trailer is disconnected from the truck, the little wheels are cranked down to hold up the front end of the trailer. The wheels allow the trailer to roll back a little as a truck backs under it.

BOTTOM: The rear wheels of the empty lumber truck are raised to prevent tire wear.

Page 13

Friction is increased by a smooth tire, since more rubber is in contact with the road. Thus, a dragster with "slicks" can accelerate faster on dry pavement. When driving through soft earth, the large cleats on tractor tires sink down, and thereby increase friction.

Page 14

TOP: The lumber company wants its name to appear to be written properly if it is seen in a car's rear view mirror.

BOTTOM: The numbers on the roof of the police cruiser permit identification of the car from a helicopter.

Page 15

TOP: 1966 Toronado

RIGHT: 1965 Mustang

LEFT: 1964 Pontiac

Page 16

The truck's cab is tipped forward when work is done on the engine underneath.

Page 17

The car shown at the bottom crashed into the back of a truck. (Notice that its bumper is not damaged.) The other car struck a tree or pole.

Page 18

A dented door is sometimes replaced with another door removed from a junked car of a different color.

Page 19

Rusting first occurs in places that are slow to dry out after the car has been driven in the rain or snow. Also, the salt that is spread on roads to melt the snow often collects on the underside of the car and makes more rust. Often these are the same spots that are missed when the undercoat of paint is applied. Do different makes of automobile rust in different places?

Page 21

Junk cars are squashed so they are easier to store and move. The cars in the upper photograph were flattened with a heavy metal plate; the car shown at the bottom was squeezed into a small cube by a giant press.

ROADS

Why were the three stones probably put in the middle of this ancient
street?

Why were the arrows
painted on the roads?

What are the lines and numbers for?

Can you explain the arrows and numbers that you see on the highway?

What happened?

Why are there
so many lines?

Did the painter make a mistake?

Why are these roads no longer used?

This old road now leads into the sea.

How long do you think these bridges have been abandoned?

As you drive, look for erosion and for ways that road builders have tried to prevent it.

Here are three places in New England where roads have been cut through rock. Which road cut is oldest?

Notice how the rocks change as you travel from one road cut to the next.

What made the lines in the rocks?

There are about 3,645,000 miles of public roads in the
United States.

How many of these do you think are dirt?

2,235,000 miles?
695,000 miles?
75,000 miles?

ANSWERS

Page 25

When it rains, water runs down the street. You can step across on the three stones without getting wet. What happens to the rain that falls on the street in front of your house?

Page 26

TOP:

The arrows show the locations of drains for rain and melted snow. After the road has been plowed, men dig out the snow bank on top of the drains.

BOTTOM:

This arrow marks the beginning of the guard fence so that snow plows can avoid hitting it.

Page 27

TOP:

The highway department is testing different kinds of paint, to find out which will last longest when used for marking the dividing line on roads.

BOTTOM LEFT:

The numbers identify a section of water pipe that runs beneath the street.

Page 27

BOTTOM RIGHT: These marks were left by surveyors to show construction crews where the road will go when it is widened.

Page 28

TOP: The manhole cover was taken off after the line was painted, and was then put back on a little twisted.

BOTTOM: This dividing line was painted three different times. Each time the driver of the line-painting machine cut the corner a little more.

Page 29

The lines were originally painted straight. The road tar was softened by the summer sun, however, and was gradually moved by the traffic.

Page 30

As roads are rebuilt and straightened out, curved sections of the old road are bypassed.

Page 32

TOP: The bridge was built in 1919 and one can assume that it was probably used for at least 20 years. Therefore, it has been abandoned less than 25 years.

BOTTOM: Judging from the size of the trees growing through it, this bridge has been unused for 10 years (and probably longer).

Page 34

The road cut pictured at the bottom left of the page is oldest; trees have had time to grow in the rocks. The cut shown in the bottom right photograph is about two years old, while the one at the top is only several months old. Notice that there is not even any grass growing at the base of the newest cut. Where in the United States would it be more difficult to tell the age of road cuts?

TOP: When blasting is done, holes are drilled into the rock and filled with dynamite charges. The lines are the remains of these holes.

BOTTOM: Between two layers of dark rock is a layer of white quartz.

There are about 2,235,000 miles of unpaved public roads in the United States. If there are so many, why do you suppose many people are unaware of this fact?

TRACKS

Which tracks were made first?

What happened here?

How many cars were there?

When a car goes over wet paint, why do the tires leave dashed lines?

Why are some dashed lines shorter than others?

What made these tracks?

Is this an entrance or an exit from the main road?

What stories might these skid marks tell?

Which way was the tractor going?

Look for other tracks and try to figure out how they were made.

ANSWERS

Page 41

The older tracks are crossed by other tracks that were made later.

Page 42

The tracks were made by an automobile turning around. The car was driven in frontwards and backed out.

Page 43

One car made these tracks by backing in to turn around.

Page 44

A band of paint sticks to a tire when it runs over a freshly painted line. The tire then acts as a rubber stamp to mark the road every time it goes around.

Page 45

Tires that went through a narrow part of the oil puddle made short lines; those going over a wider section of the puddle left longer lines. How are the dashed lines made by small tires different from those made by bigger tires?

Page 46

TOP: The two thin tracks were made by a bicycle.

BOTTOM: The location of the wet tracks indicate that cars have entered the parking lot from the road.

Page 47

TOP: These long skid marks were made by a truck. It probably had to stop suddenly to avoid hitting a car that had slowed down to turn off the road at the exit.

BOTTOM: These are scratch marks, left by a hotrodder who "popped" his clutch into low as his car rolled backwards.

The tractor was traveling from left to right. A tractor tire is put on so that the point of each "V" on the tread touches the ground before its wider part. If the treads went the other way mud would get packed against the inside of the "V", which would tend to make the tires skid more easily.

Why?

What is on the
front of these signs?

Guess what signs say before you read them.

Someone goofed!

Why are there weights hanging from the sign?

Why might this sign be blank?

It's a good thing the children don't drive fast!

Duck?

What do these signs mean?

How were the signs probably damaged?

Guess how these streets were named.

Look for signs in foreign languages.

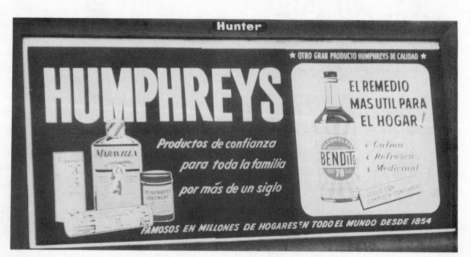

What words are spelled incorrectly on these signs?

Look for signs with misspelled words.

Where are these signs located?

Have you ever seen signs with your name?

Look for a sign with a longer word.

*Look for a signpost
with more signs.*

Do you think the inmates of this prison would agree?

What does the Eastern Co. manufacture?

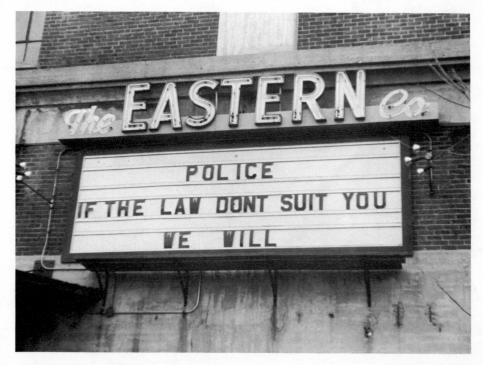

Page 52

TOP LEFT: A lower gear helps trucks slow down on hills.

TOP RIGHT: Blasting caps of dynamite charges are set off electrically. There is a slight possibility that radio waves from a car transmitter would accidently discharge a blasting cap.

BOTTOM: Because there is no warm earth beneath the bridge, the surface of the bridge freezes before the road. Why does a light snow often melt off the road before it melts from the grass?

Page 53

The shape of a sign is often a clue to what it says. In this way drivers can guess the message even before they can read it.

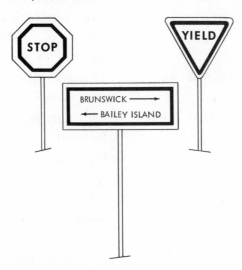

Page 55

TOP: Drivers of large trucks are more likely to notice the sign, since the weights are too low for trucks to fit underneath without hitting them. If a driver does not see the sign and drives under it, the weights make a warning noise when they hit the top of the truck.

BOTTOM: Written on the sign under a piece of canvas is: "Caution, fog ahead." This warning is uncovered by the police when the road is foggy.

Page 57

TOP: Cars traveling on the road ahead have the right of way.

MIDDLE: The highway narrows down from three lanes to two.

BOTTOM: The main road crosses another road that is difficult to see before you reach it.

Page 58

TOP LEFT: A snow plow probably scraped against the sign and bent the left corner back. The paint came off along the bend, and the bare metal soon rusted.

TOP RIGHT: The dents in the sign were made by rifle bullets and shotgun pellets.

BOTTOM: Part of this wooden sign was probably broken off by a snow plow that got too close.

Page 59

Longfellow Road: Many streets are named for famous people, such as this one in honor of Henry Wadsworth Longfellow.

Atlantic Ave: This was named for the ocean that is next to it.

Bedford Lane: This narrow road leads toward Bedford.

Deer Run: Picturesque names are often given roads in new housing developments to make the area appear more attractive to prospective home buyers.

Finn Road: A family from Finland once lived on Finn Road.

Page 61

TOP LEFT: The words "vegetables" and "ahead" are misspelled.

TOP RIGHT: "Vegetables" is spelled wrong on this sign also.

BOTTOM: "Accommodations" and "overnight" are misspelled.

Page 62

LEFT: This sign was in Charleston, South Carolina.

RIGHT: The sign is in Waterford, Maine.

Page 65   The Eastern Company manufactures uniforms.

FIRE HYDRANTS

Why does this "King of the Fire Hydrants" wear a crown?

Why are some hydrants surrounded by fences or posts?

Can you find a fire hydrant taller than you are?

Why is the hydrant so short and so far from the curb?

Which of the four fire hydrants do you think is oldest?

Notice how many different kinds of hydrants there are.

Can you find a hydrant with more than three water outlets?

Why is there a hole in the wall behind the top of the fire hydrant?

Why does this fire hydrant have a high "flag"?

The valve nut on top of a fire hydrant turns on the water. Why does the nut have five sides instead of four or six (as most other nuts have)?

Why does this hydrant have four valve nuts?

He's stronger than he looks.

ANSWERS

Page 69

The fire hydrant has a sharp top to keep people from sitting on it and blocking the store window behind.

Page 70

Fire hydrants near the road are sometimes protected from being run over by cars and trucks.

Page 71

A new sidewalk was built after the fire hydrant was installed.

Page 72

The hydrant in front of the stone wall is the oldest. Notice that this hydrant is more decorative and looks old-fashioned.

Page 74

TOP: Fire hydrants are turned on at the top with a wrench. The hole in the wall permits the wrench to be turned around in a complete circle.

BOTTOM: The raised marker shows the location of the hydrant when it is covered with snow.

Page 75

TOP: Because the valve nut is an odd shape, a special wrench is needed to turn it. This makes it harder for mischief-makers to open the hydrant.

BOTTOM: On this fire hydrant, each valve nut controls a separate water outlet. The valve nut on top of most hydrants opens all the outlets at once.

FENCES

Which way was the wind blowing?

Why does the guard rail have a groove?

How were the wires put through the tree?

Why is there a little fence sticking out from the main fence?

Why was the fence built crooked?

Here are fences made with doors and stumps.

Why is the gatepost so high on one side?

Why is there a pile of rocks on one end of this gate?

How does this "gate" keep the cattle in?

ANSWERS

Page 79

The wind was blowing from the left to the right. As the wind blows through a snow fence, its speed is reduced. When this happens, most of the snow that is being carried along by the wind falls to the ground. Would a solid snow fence work better than a slatted one?

Page 80

TOP: The groove in the guard rail greatly increases its strength.

BOTTOM: The wires were nailed to the tree a long time ago. Then, as the tree got bigger, it grew over the wires.

Page 81

TOP: The small fence that sticks out is to keep people from walking along the wall on the outside of the main fence.

BOTTOM: A zigzag fence does not require posts. There are only wires at the corners holding the rails together.

Page 83

TOP: The long diagonal strip on the gate prevents its outer edge from sagging.

BOTTOM: The rocks act to counterbalance the weight of the gate so it can be opened without lifting.

Page 84

Where the road crosses the fence line, there are a number of iron bars over a shallow hole. Cattle are instinctively afraid to walk across the slippery bars. In what way is this kind of "gate" better than a regular gate?

WIRES AND POLES

Which are electric wires and which are telephone wires?

How can you tell if a house has a telephone?

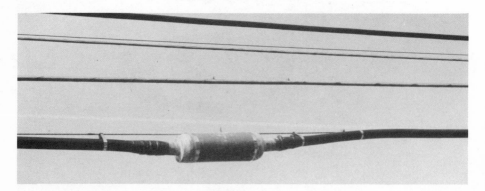

The bulge shows where the ends of two telephone wires have been spliced together.

Look at wires and see how long an uncut section of wire you can find.

Does electricity kill tree branches?

Why are the four lower wires encased in thick asbestos?

Why are there blocks of wood on the wires?

How are these wires
protected against being
chewed by squirrels?

Do all wires sag?

What made the shadows?

When is a pole supported by a wooden brace instead of a guy wire?

Do the wires stop where the poles end?

What two poles were next to one another?

What might have scarred the tree?

How can you tell this is an old scar?

Notice how few roads there are which have no wires at all.

Page 88

Electric wires are usually attached with insulators to the cross-arms near the top of poles. The telephone wire is thicker and is fastened directly to the pole about halfway up.

Page 89

The tree branches, of course, were not killed by electricity, but were cut away by linemen.

Page 90

TOP: The asbestos is to protect the telephone wires in case there is a fire in the building beside them.

BOTTOM: The blocks of wood prevent the wires from wearing as they rub against the branches.

Page 91

TOP: The men are nailing sheets of aluminum on the poles. Squirrels are unable to climb up the poles to the wires because the metal shields are too slippery.

BOTTOM: These wires are covered with screening where they are close to the trees. The short metal walls keep the squirrels from running farther along the wires.

Page 92

All wires sag since a wire would break before it could be tightened enough to make it perfectly straight. Do wires on poles that are far apart sag more than wires on poles close together?

Page 93

TOP: These shadows were made by the cross-arms of two telephone poles.

BOTTOM: The shadow comes from a blinker light suspended from a wire over an intersection.

Page 94

A guy wire only holds when it is pulled, while a wooden brace, though more expensive, is strongest when being pushed. The pole in the lower photograph had to be prevented from bending to the right. If a wire were used, it would have to stretch all the way across the road. (This is often done, however, in a manner shown in the sketch below.)

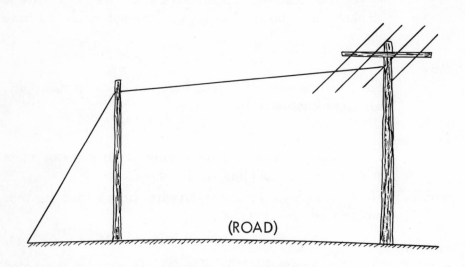

(ROAD)

Page 95

The wires continue on underground from the place where the poles stop. Look for wires that do this as you enter a city.

Page 96

The pole shown in the upper left was next to the one pictured in the lower left. Telephone poles are numbered for the purpose of identification.

Page 97

LEFT: The bark from the tree was ripped off when an automobile smashed into it.

RIGHT: See how this tree is growing over its scar.

GAME SECTION:

Things to Do While Traveling

HIGHWAY SCAVENGER HUNT

Make a list of things to look for while you are traveling. Then see who can find the most. A sample chart for score keeping is below. You can use other ideas of your own or from the photographs on the preceding pages.

	POINT VALUE	MOM	DAD	DOUG	JAY
DIRT ROAD	1				
SNOW FENCE	2				
CAR CARRYING MORE THAN EIGHT PEOPLE	2				
HOUSE WITHOUT A TELEPHONE	3				
MISSPELLED WORD ON SIGN	3				
FLAT TIRE	1				
NUMBER PAINTED ON ROAD	1				
EROSION	1				

MAKE AN ACCELEROMETER

It is easy to make an instrument for measuring how fast your car starts and stops. Get a cardboard box and cut it as shown in the drawing. Then hang a little weight on each side, and mark number scales to show how far the weights swing. Tape the accelerometer to the window of your car door and watch it.

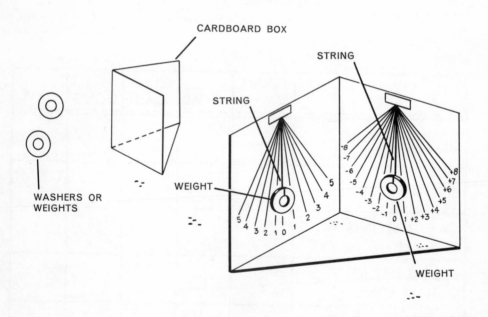

Here are some questions you should be able to answer by using your accelerometer:

What happens to the accelerometer as your car starts moving?
What does it do when you are traveling at a steady speed?
Which one of the two weights moves more?

How does your accelerometer indicate a change in speed?

Can the meter detect slight changes in speed that you are unable to feel yourself?

Can your car stop faster than it can start?

Can you accelerate more when you are moving or when you are standing still?

What does the accelerometer do when your car goes up or down a hill?

License Plate Hunt

As you travel, see how many license plates you can find from different states. Trace the United States map on a piece of paper, and pencil in each state you get.

License Plate Slogans

Rearrange the slogans so each is matched with the proper state.

1.	Scenic	a	Alabama
2.	America's Dairyland	b	Arizona
3.	Sunshine State	c	West Virginia
4.	Treasure State	d	Nebraska
5.	10,000 Lakes	e	New Jersey
6.	Heart of Dixie	f	Montana
7.	Mountain State	g	Florida
8.	Famous Potatoes	h	Hawaii
9.	Pacific Wonderland	i	Maine
10.	The Beef State	j	Idaho
11.	Grand Canyon State	k	Wisconsin
12.	Peach State	l	New Mexico
13.	Garden State	m	Louisiana
14.	Land of Enchantment	n	Arkansas
15.	Land of Lincoln	o	Oregon
16.	Winter-Water Wonderland . .	p	North Dakota
17.	Land of Opportunity	q	New Hampshire
18.	Sportsman's Paradise	r	Georgia
19.	Vacationland	s	Minnesota
20.	Peace Garden State	t	Michigan
21.	Aloha State	u	Kansas
22.	Midway U.S.A.	v	Illinois

ANSWERS

1. q. 6. a. 11. b.
2. k. 7. c. 12. r. 17. n.
3. g. 8. j. 13. e. 18. m.
4. f. 9. o. 14. l. 19. i.
5. s. 10. d. 15. v. 20. p.
16. f. 21. h.
22. u.

[107]

You can play a game with the numbers on license plates. Make up your own rules for determining how license plates will be chosen by each player. The value of different number combinations is shown below.

VALUE	NAME	EXPLANATION	EXAMPLE
WORST	HIGH NUMBER		M68–251
	PAIR	TWO NUMBERS THE SAME	82891
	TWO PAIRS		R–41515
	THREE OF A KIND	THREE NUMBERS THE SAME	21922
	FULL HOUSE	A PAIR AND THREE OF A KIND	225–455
	SEQUENCE	FIVE CONSECUTIVE NUMBERS	14–3925
	FOUR OF A KIND		22252
BEST	FIVE OF A KIND		636666

Which of these plates would win?

2M-322

492-828

646-246

19322

HEARING AND FEELING THE ROAD

Close your eyes and see what you can tell about the road. (This game is not recommended for the driver.) How does the hum of your tires change at different speeds? Why do the tires make a regular thumping sound on some concrete roads? Why are you able to tell when your car goes around a curve or up a steep hill? How steep must a slope be for you to feel it? Notice the sounds made as the car passes poles, trees, and parked cars. Where do these sounds come from?

ALPHABET SIGN GAME

The object of this game is to find words beginning with each letter of the alphabet in order, from A to Z. Team competition helps to liven up the contest. The letter X should probably be eliminated. Have you seen signs with words beginning with Q or Z? What other letters would you expect difficulty in finding?

Guess how fast you are going

Try to guess your speed before looking at the speedometer. Does 40 mph seem faster on a narrow road or on the open highway? You probably cannot run faster than 15 miles per hour. How fast does this seem in a car?

Check the accuracy of your speedometer

Turnpikes usually have small markers placed every mile. If you travel 60 mph, it should take exactly one minute to go the mile from one marker to the next. See how long it takes your car to cover a mile when you are going 60 mph. What does it mean if it takes 65 seconds instead of a minute?

Compute the speed of a car that passes you, going in the same direction

Here is how to find out how fast another car is going. Look at the second hand of a watch when the car passes. Then select a landmark (something like a bridge or large tree) on the road ahead. As the car goes by it, see how many seconds have passed, and also notice the mileage on your speedometer. Check your mileage again when you arrive at the landmark, and use the table below to figure out the passing car's speed. Add the number from the table to the speed of your car.

ADDITIONAL M.P.H. OF PASSING CAR

DISTANCE (IN TENTHS OF A MILE)
BETWEEN YOUR CAR AND LANDMARK

		.1	.2	.3	.4	.5
	10	36				
	20	18	36	54		
TIME (IN SECONDS) FOR PASSING CAR TO REACH LANDMARK	30	12	24	36	48	60
	40	9	18	27	36	45
	50	7	14	22	29	36
	60	6	12	18	24	30

Can you devise a method for measuring the speed of a car that is traveling slower than your car?

How does a speedometer work?

The diagram shows what a speedometer looks like inside. Do you understand how it works? If you can, get a speedometer out of an old car at a junk yard and take it apart.

SPEEDOMETER CABLE CONNECTS TO
THE REAR AXLE OF THE CAR

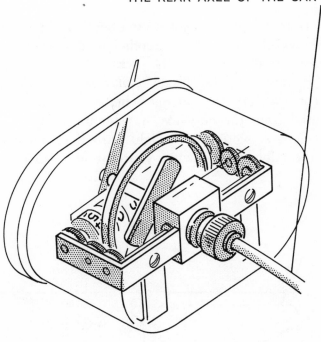

Some things to do with the odometer

Pick out something on the road ahead (such as a bridge or building), and have everyone in the car guess how far away it is. Then the exact distance can be measured with the odometer. As the game continues, the estimates should improve.

Without looking at the odometer, see if you can tell when you have gone ten miles. Would a watch help if you knew your speed?

Check your odometer with turnpike mileage markers to see how accurate it is. Does tire wear affect the odometer reading? Bear your findings in mind when you make other experiments using the odometer.

How far apart are telephone poles? Count how many there are in a mile and divide. Do this again along another road to see if poles are always spaced about the same.

Are the signs indicating the distances to towns and to turnpike exits always correct? Try to find out whether the distance to a town is measured from the city line or from the center.

What is the longest section of straight road that you can find?

What does the odometer do when your car goes backwards?

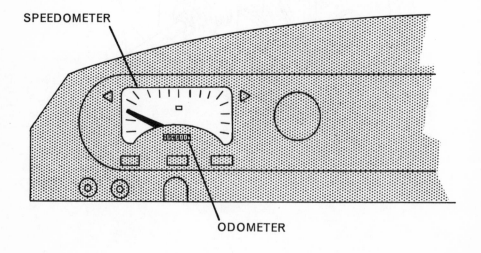

SPEEDOMETER

ODOMETER

HOW GOOD IS YOUR GAS MILEAGE?

"MY CAR IS A GAS HOG!"

Do you know how many miles your car can run on each gallon of gasoline? Here is how you can find out:

When your gas tank is filled, record the mileage on the odometer. The next time you need gas, the tank must be filled again. Use the new odometer reading to figure how far you have traveled.

Then divide the miles traveled by the gallons of gas needed to refill the tank. This gives you your gas mileage.

If you compute your gas mileage several times and take an average, you will get a more accurate answer.

How does your gas mileage compare with that of other vehicles?

VEHICLE	MILES PER GALLON OF FUEL	FUEL	LOADED WEIGHT IN TONS	SPEED IN M.P.H.
MOTOR SCOOTER	100	GASOLINE	1/5	45
MOTORCYCLE	75	GASOLINE	1/3	60
SMALL CAR	28	GASOLINE	1	60
BIG CAR	12	GASOLINE	2	70
SCHOOL BUS	10	GASOLINE	9	45
DUMP TRUCK	8	GASOLINE	20	45
TRAILER TRUCK	5	DIESEL	30	60
HELICOPTER	4	GASOLINE	1-1/2	85
FARM TRACTOR	2	GASOLINE	2	2-1/2
707 JET	3/4	KEROSENE	120	600
BULLDOZER	1/4	DIESEL	14	1
ARMY TANK	1/4	GASOLINE	40	25
OCEAN LINER	1/50	FUEL OIL	65,000	35

ROAD MAPS

Look at a road map as you travel.

> Where are you on the map?
> In what direction are you going?
> What town will you come to next?
> Where will you cross a river?
> When will you arrive at your destination?
> How far have you traveled since you left home?

Which is the best road?

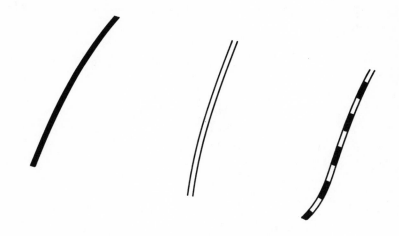

Which town is biggest?

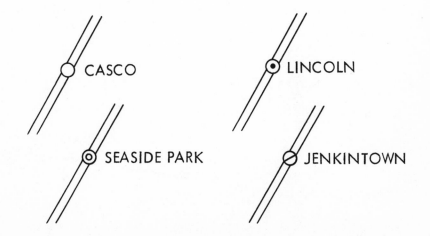

Do you know what these map symbols mean? Can you find some of them on any of your road maps?

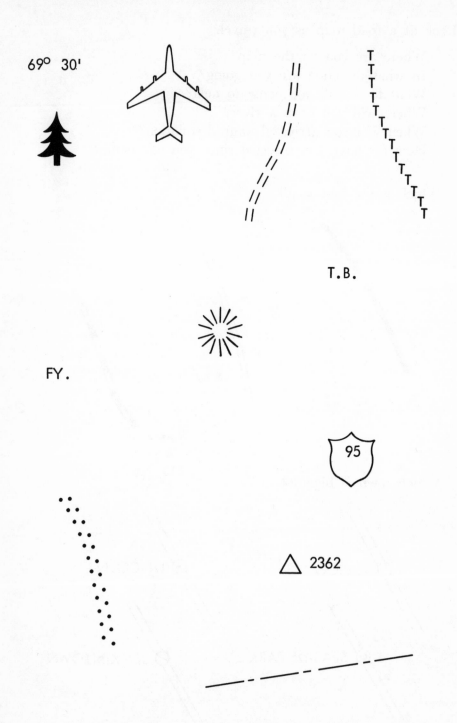

69° 30'

T.B.

FY.

95

△ 2362

SET UP A WEATHER STATION IN YOUR CAR

To measure air temperature, tape a thermometer on the outside of the car window. Put it on so you can read it from inside. You can make a chart and record the temperatures during the day.

At what time of day is it usually warmest?

TIME	TEMPERATURE
8:30	72
9:10	75
10:25	81

Should the temperature of the air be measured in the sun or in the shade?
Are hilltops ever cooler than valleys?
How does the temperature where you are compare with the temperature at other places (as given on weather reports over the car radio)?
Does the thermometer always go up when the car stops?

Is the wind colder?

Hold your hand out the window when the car is stopped and again when you are traveling fast. If you take the temperature of the outside air when the car is stopped and again when it is going, you will see that it is always about the same. Why does the air feel colder when you are moving?

Calibrating an anemometer

An anemometer is an instrument for measuring the speed of the wind. Here is how to make a simple anemometer.

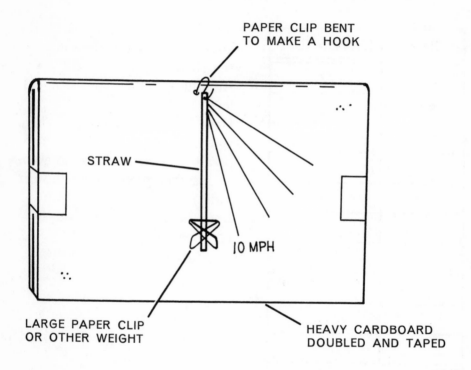

PAPER CLIP BENT
TO MAKE A HOOK

STRAW

10 MPH

LARGE PAPER CLIP
OR OTHER WEIGHT

HEAVY CARDBOARD
DOUBLED AND TAPED

After your anemometer is built, it will be necessary to put on a scale to indicate the wind's speed. (This is known as calibration.) To calibrate the anemometer, hold it facing toward you, a few inches out the car window and have someone drive at 5 mph. Then make a mark on the cardboard underneath the straw. Continue doing this while going 10, 15, 20, 30, 40, and 50. Why is the space between o mph amd 10 mph not the same as the space between 20 mph and 30 mph? Why should you calibrate your anemometer on a day when there is not much wind?

Now you can use the anemometer to measure the speed of the wind when you are not in the car. Also, it will work as a speedometer when held out the car window. Do airplanes measure their speed this way?

North-south temperature changes

If you are traveling to the north or south, look for signs of temperature change. In the spring, tree leaves appear earlier to the south. Even a distance of a few hundred miles north or south can make a noticeable change. The amount of snow on the ground also changes greatly from one spot to another.

Differences in elevation have an effect on local temperature too. Sometimes pronounced variations in snow cover or plant budding can be observed in two locations only a few miles apart.

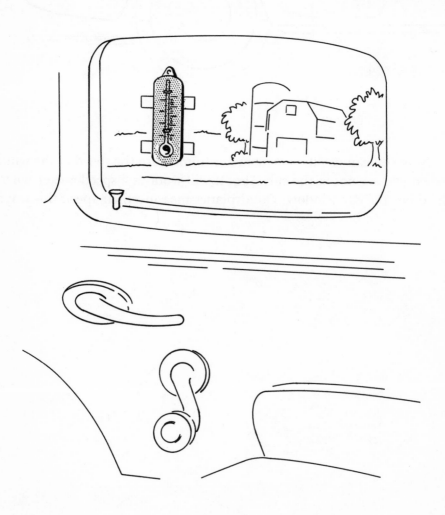

Using a barometer as an altimeter

A barometer is a weather instrument that measures air pressure. Changes in air pressure often indicate changing weather conditions. An altimeter measures height; airplanes have altimeters to tell how high they are above sea level. You can use a weather barometer as an altimeter in your car.

Take a barometer with you on an automobile trip. See how much it changes as you climb big hills and go down into valleys. The air pressure is less on the tops of hills since there is less air up high. A barometer drops about 1 inch of mercury for every 1000 feet that you go up. Try to estimate the height of hills by changes in air pressure.

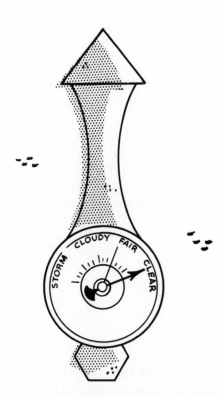

Weather prediction

As you drive, look for signs of weather conditions ahead. Sometimes it is not raining or snowing where you are, but cars coming toward you have their windshield wipers going or they are covered with snow. Also, puddles on the road may mean you are catching up with a rain storm.

Clouds

Look for shadows of clouds on the road. In which direction are the clouds going? How fast are they moving? If the clouds are traveling in about the same direction as your car, see if you can measure their speed with the speedometer.

ANIMALS ALONG THE ROAD

With the speedometer, you can find the speed of running and flying animals. How fast can a dog run when he chases your car? (Sometime have a race with your car to see how fast you can run.) Watch birds as they fly along beside the car. Do big birds fly faster than little ones?

You can tell what wildlife lives in the area you are driving through by looking on the road for animals that have been run over. Among the animals that are most frequently killed are woodchucks, skunks, and rabbits. How do these animals normally protect themselves? Why are raccoons, foxes, and cats less likely to be hit by cars?

Make a high-speed bug catcher

You can catch a lot of flying insects by putting a piece of window screening between the grill and radiator of your car. Bend the screen forward at the bottom to catch bugs that drop down.

After a day's drive, remove your bug catcher and see what you have caught. How many different kinds of insects can you identify? Do you find many more insects on some days than on others?

You might want to make a collection of the bugs you catch with your car.

HOUSEHOLD SCREENING

GRILL

Here is the worst bug on the highway

Don't **YOU** be a
LITTERBUG!

DAVID WEBSTER is well known to the 250,000 readers of *Nature and Science* Magazine as the creator of each issue's Brain Boosters and other popular features. He is a former elementary and junior high school science teacher and served for four years as Director of Science for the Lincoln, Massachusetts, school system. He is now a staff writer and teacher for the Elementary Science Study of Educational Services Incorporated, which is engaged in producing science units for children in the elementary grades.

A man of boundless energy and imagination, Mr. Webster is co-owner and co-director of Camp Netop, a boys' camp in Maine, and he has been a Boy Scout leader for many years. Mr. Webster and his family live in Lincoln, Massachusetts.

10-2-67